I HERO

3 1 AUG 2016

2 2 OCT 2018

WITHDRAWN

BLOOD CROWN QUEST
DEMON SEA

Steve Barlow and Steve Skidmore
Illustrated by Jack Lawrence

EDGE

First published in 2013
by Franklin Watts

Text © Steve Barlow and Steve Skidmore 2013
Illustrations by Jack Lawrence © Franklin Watts 2013
Cover design by Jonathan Hair

Franklin Watts
338 Euston Road
London NW1 3BH

Franklin Watts Australia
Level 17/207 Kent Street
Sydney, NSW 2000

The authors and illustrator have asserted their rights in
accordance with the Copyright, Designs and Patents Act, 1988.

A CIP catalogue record for this book
is available from the British Library.

(ebook) ISBN: 978 1 4451 1505 4
(pb) ISBN: 978 1 4451 1501 6
(Library ebook) ISBN: 978 1 4451 2523 7

1 3 5 7 9 10 8 6 4 2

Printed and bound by
CPI Group (UK) Ltd, Croydon, CR0 4YY

Franklin Watts is a division of Hachette Children's Books,
an Hachette UK company.
www.hachette.co.uk

How to be a hero

This book is not like others you may have read. You are the hero of this adventure. It is up to you to make decisions that will affect how the adventure unfolds.

Each section of this book is numbered. At the end of most sections, you will have to make a choice. The choice you make will take you to a different section of the book.

Some of your choices will help you to complete the adventure successfully. But choose carefully, some of your decisions could be fatal!

If you fail, then start the adventure again and learn from your mistake.

If you choose correctly you will succeed in your mission.

Don't be a zero, be a hero!

The quest so far...

You are a skilled warrior, living in a world of enchantment and danger. Humans live alongside trolls, elves and dwarves, while other mysterious creatures walk in the shadows.

The Queen of Alba has asked for your help against her deadliest foes — the Red Queen and her husband, Mortha, the necromancer.

Many years ago, Solmor, the world's greatest Spellcaster, created a crown of gold set with four great rubies. The Ruby of Power gave its owner fighting skills. The Ruby of Seeing, the gift of telepathy and reading minds. The Ruby of Magic, powers of enchantment. The Ruby of Death, mastery over the world of the dead.

But rulers across the world wanted the power of the Crown of Rubies for themselves. It became a force for evil and was renamed the Blood Crown.

Just before his death, Solmor destroyed the crown and had the rubies hidden across the globe, so no one could find them.

But the Red Queen and her necromancer

husband are hunting for them. They already possess the Ruby of Death. If they succeed in finding the others, your world will be plunged into a new dark age.

By your daring, you have recovered the Ruby of Power and the Ruby of Seeing. Your companion, Olderon, was not so lucky. He was killed by servants of the Red Queen.

You are now searching for the Ruby of Magic. To recover it, you must travel to the Sea of Oblivion and find the Old Man of the Sea, who is the guardian of the ruby.

Go to 1.

1

You have spent many hours flying on your gryphon, Hergal, but now you are approaching the port of Yushan. Beyond the port lies the vast Sea of Oblivion, home to many strange creatures and the haunt of deadly pirates.

You have used the Ruby of Seeing to make your way here, but when you try to ask it where to find the Old Man of the Sea, it shows only mist and shadows. It is getting dark and you have to decide whether you will continue flying, or land in the port. There you might find someone who knows of his whereabouts, or you might run into the Red Queen's servants.

If you wish to continue flying, go to 18.
If you wish to land, go to 36.

2

You tell your story to the Old Man of the Sea.

He nods. "So you want me to simply give you the Ruby of Magic?"

"It is not for me. My quest is to stop the Red Queen, and to save the world..."

"Your world, not mine," replies the Old Man.

"If the Red Queen finds the rubies, she will be ruler of land, sky and sea."

The Old Man of the Sea considers your words. "Very well." He gestures to Narwul, who goes to a great wooden chest next to the throne. He opens it. It is full of treasure, and lying among the jewels and coins is the Ruby of Magic. The Old Man of the Sea takes it out. "But are you worthy of such power?" he asks. "You have already lost the other two rubies to me. Can you be trusted with this quest?"

If you wish to persuade the Old Man to give you the ruby, go to 11.

If you decide to try to take it by force, go to 28.

3

You leave the inn and head down towards the harbour.

A heavy sea mist hangs in the air. You hear the sounds of creaking ropes and shouts as sailors load up the ships with cargo. As you wander through the harbour, a man steps out from behind a stack of crates. He holds a flaming torch. "Can I help you?" he asks.

"I seek passage on a ship," you reply.

"Oh, we can provide that, can't we lads?"

From out of the mist, a dozen armed men appear. Before you can react, you are clubbed to the ground and pass out.

Go to 12.

4

You hold up your hands. "I meant no..."

But before you can finish your sentence there is a flash of steel and you drop to the ground. The man has run you through! You clutch at your stomach as the man snatches the leather pouch holding the two rubies from around your neck.

Without the Ruby of Power, you are unable to defend yourself as the jeering crowd surrounds you. As your energy seeps away, fists hammer down on you. There is nothing you can do against so many people.

Your quest has failed — the Red Queen is victorious! Put a stop to her plans next time. Get back to 1.

5

You open your eyes and for a moment think you must be dead! You are lying on a bed in a room, which has a huge glass wall looking out onto the depths of the sea. You realise that you are in some sort of glass building on the sea floor. You get out of the bed and stand at the window and watch fish and mer-people swimming.

At that moment, the door opens and a creature steps inside.

You are amazed at his appearance. He is over three metres tall and has a pair of sharp tusks growing out of his cheeks. A silver fin runs down the length of his back. He is armed with a trident and has your leather pouch containing the two rubies tied to his belt.

"My name is Narwul. You will come with me," he growls. "My master wishes to meet you."

If you wish to do as he says, go to 26.

If you wish to try to get the rubies back, go to 32.

6

In the blink of an eye, you draw your sword. You kick a ghoul dwarf out of your path, and confront the ghoul captain. He sneers at you, just before you run him through with your blade.

The other ghouls stop where they are. Something is wrong. The ghoul captain is still standing in front of you, and now he's smiling. The sound of the undead crew laughing fills the air.

"You'll have to do a lot better than that!"

he rasps. The captain pulls your sword out of his chest and offers it to you.

"Do you want another try?"

You take back your sword.

"All right you scurvy-ridden lot. Shut up!" he shouts at the cackling crew. They fall silent.

"That's enough playing around," the ghoul captain says. "Give me the rubies."

If you want to do as the ghoul captain says, go to 39.

If you wish to continue to fight, go to 17.

7

You spin Hergal around, but the gryphon cannot outfly the zombie birds. They engulf you and rip at your flesh.

Hergal roars out in pain as the birds continue their attack. You slash at your enemies with your sword, but it is hopeless, there are too many of them! Their rotting bodies swarm all over you. Mercifully you pass into blackness.

You've become bird feed! To begin your quest again, go back to 1.

8

You use the Ruby of Power to help you slowly break free of the Old Man of the Sea's grip. But before you can escape with the rubies, the dome above you breaks open and the sea thunders in. The cold water engulfs you and the Old Man of the Sea.

The rubies are ripped from your hand by the force of the torrent, and you soon realise that you are doomed.

Water pours into your mouth and fills your lungs. The Sea of Oblivion has claimed another victim.

You have failed at the last hurdle! Don't let the Red Queen win. Get back to 1.

9

Carefully, you creep off the ship. Luckily the pirates are too busy getting ready to set sail to notice you leaving. You head back to the square.

Calling on the power of the Ruby of Seeing, you see Hergal lying outside the port, sleeping. You give a whistle and the gryphon wakes.

Minutes later she lands in the square and you are soon flying on Hergal's back, heading across the moonlit sea.

As the sun rises higher in the east, you hear a great roaring noise ahead of you. The wind gains strength and buffets you, and Hergal struggles to stay on course. Sea spray whips across your face and you are forced to shield your eyes as you attempt to see where the wind is coming from. You know that something is not right!

Go to 44.

10

You head through the dark streets of Yushan, following the directions to the inn. There is hardly a soul around, and a grey mist is drifting in from the sea. You turn a corner and see a beggar sheltering in a doorway. As you approach he holds out his hand, "Spare a coin for a poor man?"

The man clearly needs help, so you reach into your purse. The Ruby of Seeing causes an image to flash into your mind, showing the

beggar for what he really is — a were-rat! You ready yourself for a fight.

The beggar transforms into its true form of a giant rat and leaps at you. It has long, black claws and gnarly pointed teeth. You know that were-beasts can only be defeated by removing their head.

If you want to attack it with your sword, go to 25.

If you want to shoot using your bow and arrows, go to 29.

11

"I have managed to find two rubies and defeated many of the Red Queen's followers," you say.

"Hmmm," murmurs the Old Man. "But I now have all three rubies." A greedy, calculating look flashes across the Old Man's face. You wonder if the Old Man of the Sea wishes to take the rubies for himself.

He continues. "In order to prove yourself worthy of the Rubies, I will set you a trial. That way I will know that you are the person to challenge the Red Queen."

You wish you had the Ruby of Seeing to tell you what the Old Man is planning. You do not really trust him, but you need the rubies back!

If you agree to the trial, go to 24.
If you don't want to take the Old Man's trial, go to 41.

12

Some time later, you wake up. It is dark. Although you are still dazed, you realise that you are inside a wooden barrel.

You thump at the sides and the lid, but cannot break free. Holes have been drilled into the sides, and the lid has been nailed down! You feel for the pouch containing the rubies, but it has been taken. You hear voices and you shout out as you feel the barrel being lifted up and thrown into the air.

Then there is a tremendous splash — you have been thrown into the sea! You are helpless as water pours in through the holes in the barrel and slowly sinks, sending you to oblivion.

To begin your quest again, go to 1.

You place your hand on the leather pouch
containing the rubies.

"What is my destiny?" you ask.

Immediately an image forms in your mind.
You see hundreds of waves crashing against
a shoreline. Olderon, your dead companion,

stands on the beach and says, *"Remember this!"* Then the vision is replaced by an image of you diving down into the depths of the ocean. Olderon's voice echoes through your mind, *"Now go. Seek out what is below."*

The image disappears and once again you see the wolf sharks circling around you.

If you wish to follow the advice in the vision from the ruby, go to 21.

If you don't want to, go to 37.

14

"I am seeking passage across the Sea of Oblivion," you tell the man. "I am looking for the Old Man of the Sea."

The man laughs. "Then you are wasting your time! No such person exists! He is just a legend!" The crowd nod and laugh in agreement. "Why would you seek him?"

You shake your head. "That is not your business," you say. "And if he doesn't exist, then there is no point telling you what my business is with him. Now get out of my way."

The man draws his sword. "You should watch

that mouth of yours. Maybe you need to learn some manners, eh?"

If you wish to apologise to the man, in the hope he'll put away his sword, go to 4.

If you wish to tell him tell him about your quest for the Blood Crown, go to 40.

If you'd rather draw your sword and defend yourself, go to 47.

15

You wake to find yourself in a cell. Blood stains your clothes and your body is racked with pain. You sit for some time wondering what will happen.

A small window in the door opens and you make out the face of Narwul. "Hurting, are you?" he growls. "Don't worry, the pain won't last for long. We're going to feed you to the fishes very soon."

The window slams shut leaving you to imagine the horrors that await you...

Your quest has failed. To begin the adventure again, go to 1.

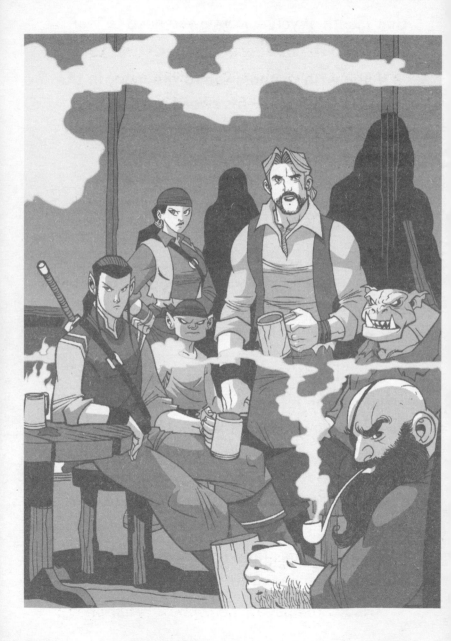

16

You leave the innkeeper and head over to a group of sailors sitting by a blazing fire.

"Greetings, friends," you begin.

They stop talking and stare at you. The largest of them stands up. "What makes you think we are your friends?"

You throw a gold coin on the table. "Well, if we are not friends, perhaps I could buy some information off you."

The sailor picks up the coin and bites it to check that it's real. He smiles. "Speak..."

"I am searching for a ship to take me across the Sea of Oblivion."

The man nods. "I know of a ship that leaves tomorrow. Be at the harbour wall at sunrise. I will see you there."

You thank the sailors and decide to turn in for the night.

Go to 42.

17

"You'll have to kill me first," you tell the captain.

"Happy to oblige," he replies. "First one to

get the rubies gets a barrel of grog!" he shouts.

The ghoul crew don't waste a second and charge at you. You strike at the creatures, but whenever you make a hit, they just drop to the floor before rising up and continuing their attack. You are forced backwards as the creatures move in.

Just as you think it is all over for you, the ship begins to rock violently. The ghouls are thrown across the deck as a massive wave crashes over the pirate ship.

You look up and see an enormous creature emerging from the depths of the sea. It is an Umibozu, a deadly sea spirit! Its pincer hands grab at the ghoul pirates and thrust them into its huge mouth.

You have a chance to escape!

If you want to hide on the ship, go to 30.
If you want to dive overboard, go to 43.

18

You urge Hergal through the blackness of the sky. Below you, the Sea of Oblivion stretches out for thousands of miles. You realise that searching for the Old Man of the Sea is like

looking for a needle in a haystack!

As you head across the sea, you hear a faint roaring noise. You continue on your way but the noise gets louder and louder. You feel the wind and sea spray ripping at your body. Hergal's wings beat faster as she tries to battle through the raging elements.

If you wish to turn back to Yushan, go to 36.
If you wish to carry on, go to 44.

19

As the waters of the Sea of Oblivion crash around, you once more call on the power of the Ruby of Magic to help you.

In the presence of the other two rubies, the power of the Ruby of Magic is immense. There is a flash of brilliant blue-white light as you feel yourself being ripped apart. Stars burst around you in a kaleidoscope of colour.

Then there is blackness

Sometime later, you wake up. You move your hand and feel sand beneath your body. You open your eyes and see Hergal standing above you. The gryphon bends her head and looks at you quizzically.

You get to your feet and pat Hergal. "I am glad to see you, my friend," you say.

Your leather pouch containing all the rubies hangs around your neck. The Ruby of Magic has kept them safe! You open the pouch and take out all three of the precious stones.

Now where to? you wonder...

Go to 50.

You head out of the inn and step into the sea mist that is covering the city. You make your way down to the harbour wall for your meeting.

As the sun rises across the sea, you hear the sound of approaching footsteps. You grip your sword as the sailor from the inn steps out of the mist. "So you survived your stay at the inn," he grunts. "Not many do. Follow me."

You do as he says and soon find yourself standing by a gangplank to a large sailing ship. The sailor gives a whistle and shortly afterwards a dwarf wearing an eye patch walks down the gangplank towards you.

The sailor points at you. "This traveller needs passage across the Sea of Oblivion."

The dwarf nods. "Come on board. You can meet the captain." He nods at the sailor, who turns and disappears into the mist.

If you wish to go on board, go to 46.
If you think this is a bad idea, go to 34.

Taking a deep breath, you plunge downwards. The wolf sharks follow you and move in for the kill.

You kick on down into the depths and your lungs feel close to bursting.

Just as you are about to pass out, you see a light below. It gets closer and you can make out the figures of several mer-people armed with

blowpipes and crossbow harpoons. They shoot at the wolf sharks, who begin to attack the mer-people.

You don't see the outcome of the battle. You cannot hold your breath any longer. Your mouth opens and you feel water pour into your lungs before you pass out into blackness.

Go to 5.

22

You take up your bow and begin to shoot at the zombie birds. You hit several of your attackers, but there are too many for you to deal with. They swarm all over you and rip at Hergal's flesh. The gryphon roars out in agony and plunges down towards the sea. You lose your grip and are thrown into the air.

Before you hit the sea, you find yourself being sucked into the mouth of the giant waterspout. Mercifully, water fills your lungs and you breathe your last.

The sea has lived up to its name, and sent you to oblivion! To begin again, go to 1.

23

You trust in the Ruby of Power to help you overcome the pirates if it comes to a fight, so you decide to stay on the ship.

The ship leaves Yushan and you head up on deck to watch the land slowly disappear from view.

Some time later, the pirate captain approaches you. The rest of the crew are standing behind him.

"Sadly, you have reached your journey's end," he snarls and draws his cutlass. "I believe you have some very precious stones. My mistress wants them!"

The crew begin to transform before your eyes! They are ghouls! You realise that you asked the Ruby of Seeing the wrong question. You asked, "Are these sailors pirates?" rather than, "Show me these men's true nature..." If you had done so, you would know that they are the undead, and that they follow the Red Queen!

To fight the undead pirates, go to 6.
To hand over the rubies, go to 39.

"Very well," you reply. "I accept your offer. We will fight."

The Old Man of the Sea laughs. "You could never defeat me in battle — especially as I have the Ruby of Power. Instead, I will test your mental strength. I will set you a riddle. If you can answer it, then I will give you the Ruby of Magic."

"And what if I can't?" you inquire.

"Perhaps we won't have to worry if you answer correctly." The Old Man begins:

"The Moon is my father,
the Sea is my mother;
I have hundreds of brothers and sisters,
I die when I reach land.
What am I?"

You remember the vision you had after diving overboard into the sea. You smile. "The answer is, a wave." You hold out your hand. "I am correct. I claim my prize."

The Old Man of the Sea is surprised, but he hands you the Ruby of Magic as he promised.

"And the other two..." you add.

He shakes his head. "Ah, I did not say that I would give you the other two rubies. You lost them to me. They are mine to keep, and you will never get them back!"

If you wish to attack the Old Man of the Sea, go to 28.

If you wish to grab the Ruby of Power that is balanced on the throne, go to 41.

If you wish to use the Ruby of Magic, go to 35.

25

In one movement you spin away from your enemy's attack and pull your sword from its sheath. The magic of the Ruby of Power surges through your body and you expertly duck under the were-rat's claws. In one clean action you swing your sword up and slice off the beast's head. It rolls into the gutter.

Yushan is a dangerous place! You decide to head to the inn quickly, before anything else tries to attack you.

Go to 33.

You realise that Narwul is too powerful for you.

"As you wish," you reply.

He leads the way through corridors. Above you, stingrays swim across the glass ceiling. Eventually you arrive at a chamber. Ahead of you is an old man sitting on a throne made of huge shells. He has a crab-claw hand and a seabird foot. Sea creatures of many shapes and sizes surround him. Most of them are armed.

Narwul hands the man the leather pouch containing the rubies. He takes them out and places them on the side of the throne. Then his eyes turn on you.

"Who are you?" he asks.

You tell him your name. "Are you the Old Man of the Sea?" you continue.

The man smiles. "That is one of the many names I have been called through the ages. I understand that my people rescued you from the wolf sharks. What brings you to the Sea of Oblivion?"

If you wish to tell him the truth, go to 2.
If you don't think you should, go to 48.

27

"My business here is not for you to know," you reply. "Now, leave me alone."

The man shakes his head. "I don't think so. We don't want your sort around here." He turns to the crowd. "Why don't you get back on your bird and go back to where you came from?"

The crowd murmur in agreement. The man pulls out his sword and points it at you.

If you wish to apologise, go to 4.

If you wish to fight the man, go to 47.

28

You leap towards the Old Man of the Sea, but he was expecting your attack.

His crab arm grabs you as the other one transforms into a long tentacle, and you are engulfed in his grasp. He pulls you towards him as his head changes to look like a shark's. His mouth opens revealing rows and rows of razor-sharp teeth.

You are helpless as you are pulled into the mouth and consumed.

You have failed in your quest, go back to 1.

29

You reach for your bow, but are too slow. The creature slashes your cheek with its claws.

You scream in pain as the were-rat plunges its teeth into your neck. The Ruby of Power fills you with strength and you grab the creature's jaw and prise it apart. The bones break with a crunch. The were-rat drops to the ground. You draw your sword and slice off its head.

But your own wound is mortal. The power of the rubies cannot help you any more. You drop to the floor in a half death, because you know that when the hour is right, you'll wake again — as a were-rat!

To restart your adventure, return to 1.

30

As the Umibozu continues its attack, you head for your cabin. But as you do, a figure steps into your path.

"Going somewhere?"

Before you can react, you feel a sharp pain rip through your body. You look down and see the captain's sword sticking into your gut! You drop to the deck.

The captain grins. "I'll be having those precious stones," he growls. It is the last thing you hear as you pass into oblivion.

You've been skewered! To begin your quest again, go to 1.

31

You make your way out of the inn. Few people are up at this hour, and you head into a small square between the houses.

Calling on the power of the Ruby of Seeing, you see Hergal lying outside the port, sleeping. You give a whistle and the gryphon awakes. She quickly takes to the air.

Minutes later Hergal lands in the square and you are soon flying on her back, heading across the blackness of the sea.

As the sun begins to rise in the east, you hear a great roaring noise ahead. The wind gains strength and blasts your body. This is not a normal storm!

Go to 44.

32

You leap at Narwul. However, he reacts with
lightning speed and smashes you away with the
trident. You fly across the room, hit the glass
wall and crash to the floor. You do not have the
Ruby of Power, and he is too strong for you.

Narwul stands over you. "Do not be so
foolish, human. I ask you again to come with
me..."

If you wish to do as he says, go to 26.
If you wish to continue the fight, go to 45.

33

You arrive at the inn and open the door. Inside,
the noisy chatter of voices goes quiet as the
occupants stare at you. You grip the hilt of your
sword, but the conversation soon strikes up
again. You are just another face in a port full
of strangers.

You walk over to the innkeeper, who is behind
the bar. He is a grobblin — a cross between a
troll and a goblin. "Good evening. I'm looking
for food and lodgings for the night."

The innkeeper nods. "That'll be two silver

coins. In advance, of course."

You pay and glance around the room. Sailors from many nations are standing, drinking and retelling tales of past voyages they have made. You turn back to the innkeeper. "Do you know of any ship that might give me passage across the Sea of Oblivion? I am searching for the Old Man of the Sea."

The grobblin's eyes narrow. "I know of no such person," he replies. "And I have no time to answer any more of your foolish questions."

If you wish to talk to the sailors, go to 16.

If you wish to head to your room to sleep, go to 42.

If you decide to ask the innkeeper more questions, go to 49.

34

"Stepping onto a boat full of strangers, is not for me," you say, turning away.

"Then I'll have to make you," says the dwarf. There is a blur of movement and you feel your legs being pulled from under you as he strikes with his weapon. You crash to the floor causing the leather pouch holding the rubies to spill open. The dwarf's eyes light up at the sight of the precious stones.

He leaps at you and smashes your head with his club. You pass into blackness.

Go to 12.

35

The Old Man of the Sea grins. "In fact, I think I will keep all three rubies after all." He gestures to Narwul, who moves towards you with his trident pointing at your chest.

Holding the Ruby of Magic, you close your eyes and whisper, "By the power of this ruby, I ask for aid."

At that moment a great shadow is cast across the room. Everyone looks up to see the Umibozu outside the dome. The creature hammers at the glass with his powerful pincers.

A crack begins to split along the glass. Water trickles in through the roof. Screams echo inside the dome.

Outside, mer-people try to fight off the sea spirit, but it is too powerful for them. The Umibozu continues its attack. The dome breaks open more and sea water rushes in, sweeping away Narwul and the other guards.

Taking this opportunity, you pounce on the Old Man of the Sea, grabbing the two rubies from his throne.

As you do so, the Old Man transforms before your eyes. His arms turn into dozens of tentacles and engulf you in a deadly grasp.

"I will have the rubies," he hisses. His mouth opens, revealing rows of razor-sharp teeth. He pulls you towards them.

If you wish to use the Ruby of Power, go to 8.

If you wish to use the Ruby of Magic, go to 19.

You decide that it will be best to land. You direct Hergal towards Yushan and land near the harbour.

Your arrival creates a stir, and soon a crowd of people gather around to stare at you and the gryphon. Some mutter angrily about witchcraft, others cast envious eyes at Hergal. You realise that you cannot leave her with these people.

By using the power of the Ruby of Seeing,

you communicate with the gryphon. You tell Hergal to fly out of the port and be ready for your return. She obeys, and heads off.

One of the crowd steps forward. "Hey, you there. What brings you to Yushan on the back of that beast?" he asks.

If you wish to tell this stranger the truth, go to 14.

If you don't want to tell him anything, go to 27.

37

You thrash at the water as you try to swim away from the wolf sharks, but the creatures are too fast.

They twist and turn in the water in excitement. You let out a scream as one of the wolf sharks bites into your leg.

Your blood pours out, sending the sharks into a feeding frenzy. They move in for the kill, and the dark water turns to red foam.

You've become dinner for the wolf sharks! To start your quest again, go to 1.

38

You don't need the Ruby of Seeing to know that he is lying! "So where is the food?" you ask.

With a snarl, the grobblin rushes at you but you are too quick for him. Your sword pierces his body and he falls to the floor.

"You will never find the Old Man of the Sea. The Red Queen will stop you," he gasps with his last breath.

You look around to check that no one has heard the scuffle, and then drag the body of the innkeeper into your room.

You decide to leave the inn immediately!

If you spoke to the sailors in the inn, go to 20.

If you didn't speak to the sailors, but wish to search for a ship, go to 3.

If you want to fly across the sea on Hergal, go to 31.

39

"I will give you the rubies, if you let me live..." you say.

The captain laughs and shakes his head.

"You are in no position to negotiate. And, to be honest, I was only being polite. We'll just take them!"

In an instant, the undead crew charge towards you. There are just too many to fight, and you are quickly overcome. You feel several bites on your arms before you pass out.

Hours later you awake and look at your body. You are dressed in pirate clothes! You have become one of the undead crew, destined to sail the Sea of Oblivion forever.

The Red Queen's minions have defeated you. Put a stop to her evil plans and get back to 1.

40

"I am on a quest for the Queen of Alba in her fight against the Red Queen and her husband, Mortha."

At the mention of their names the crowd look worried and begin to move away. The man sheathes his sword. "Then I have found someone who is crazier than most adventurers. Luck be with you! But if I were you, I'd find a bed for the night. There are strange creatures that walk the streets of Yushan after dark. If you head to the square, there is an inn. Stay there until daybreak..." Before you can ask any more questions, he hurries away.

If you wish to head to the inn, go to 33.
If you wish to find a ship, go to 3.

41

"I don't think so!" you cry out. You dive for the Ruby of Power that is balanced on the side of the throne. You know it will give you a chance. Narwul knocks you down before you get close. You grab hold of his trident — taking him by surprise — and wrestle it from his grasp. He responds by diving at you and piercing you with his tusks. You cry out in pain as the sharp ivory points tear through your skin.

You kick at him, sending him sprawling. The other sea creatures move in as you try to reach for the Ruby of Power, but you are too slow.

As you grasp for the throne, the Old Man of the Sea transforms before your eyes. His arms turn into dozens of tentacles and you are engulfed in his grasp. He squeezes you, forcing the breath out of your body and you pass out into blackness.

Go to 15.

42

You head up to your room and settle in for the night.

Some hours later, you wake suddenly. You can hear someone on the other side of the bedroom door. Silently, you get out of bed and reach for your sword.

You make your way to the door. Someone is trying to get into the room! You grab the handle and fling open the door.

The innkeeper is in the hallway; he is holding a candle.

You step forward. "What are you doing?" you demand.

"I was bringing your food!" he growls. "You made me jump!"

If you believe him, go to 49.

If you don't believe him, go to 38.

As the Umibozu continues its attack, you run to the ship's rail and are just about to dive overboard, when a hand grabs your shoulder.

"Why are you in such a hurry to leave?"

It's the pirate captain!

You try to twist out of his grasp, but it's no good. Suddenly, one of the Umibozu's pincer hands latches onto the captain and tugs him away. You quickly turn and dive overboard into the raging sea.

As you swim away you hear a howling sound, coming from beneath the waves. You look down

and see dozens of fins heading towards you. The howling gets louder. It is a pack of wolf sharks! Your blood turns cold; these creatures can strip the flesh from a body in seconds!

The wolf sharks begin to circle around you.

If you wish to try to swim away from the creatures, go to 37.

If you wish to use the Ruby of Seeing, go to 13.

44

You drive Hergal forward, but the gryphon makes little progress. The roaring gets louder and the spray from the sea drenches you.

You suddenly realise why! Ahead of you are two giant waterspouts. They twist and turn, sucking up water from the sea hundreds of metres into the sky.

You change course, but to your horror, you find that they follow you! You realise that these are no ordinary waterspouts, they are giant living water creatures! As they close in on you, they open their huge gaping mouths and hundreds of decaying zombie sea birds fly out.

They head towards you with their great beaks open!

If you wish to turn back, go to 7.
If you want to fight the creatures, go to 22.

45

"I will have my rubies back," you say as you leap up and grab hold of the trident. You try to force Narwul backwards, but he is too strong for you.

He throws you to the floor and presses down with the trident across your chest. You struggle to free yourself but his tusks are at your throat. Slowly the ivory presses into your flesh.

You let out a brief scream as your throat is punctured and you pass out in pain.

Go to 15.

46

You know that it is a risk to go on board, but you are sure that the Ruby of Power will help you overcome any attackers.

You follow the dwarf up the gangplank and onto the ship. He takes you to the captain's cabin. "Captain, this traveller wishes to come with us across the Sea of Oblivion."

The captain looks at you. "Very well. We can give you passage today. But it will cost you ten gold pieces."

You nod and give the captain the gold. "Welcome on board. Show our friend here around," the captain tells the dwarf. "We cast off in an hour."

You head out onto the deck. There are about

twelve members of the crew. They stare at you as you make your way to your quarters.

The dwarf shows you a small cabin. "This is where you'll sleep," he says, and then leaves.

You lock the door and take out the Ruby of Seeing. "Are these sailors pirates?" you ask it.

Images of the crew attacking ships and stealing treasure flood into your mind. Your hunch was right — you are on a pirate ship!

If you want to get off the ship immediately, go to 9.

If you wish to stay on the ship, go to 23.

47

You pull out your sword just as the man thrusts forwards. The crowd moves back as a fight begins; the clang of your sword blades echoes in the night. You feel the Ruby of Power glow, and you twist and hook the man's sword from his grasp. It clatters onto the ground. The man scrambles for his weapon, but you are too quick for him. In an instant your sword is at his throat. "I said my business is none of yours. Do you agree?"

The man nods his head.

You turn to the crowd. "Does anyone else wish to disagree with me?"

They shake their heads and move away.

You turn back to the man. "Now tell me where I can find lodging for the night."

The terrified man tells you where to find the best inn in town.

"Now be gone, and remember your manners." You kick his backside, sending him on his way, and then head to the inn.

Go to 10.

48

You decide not to tell the Old Man the truth.

"I was captured by pirates and they held me prisoner. I was cast overboard when an Umibozu attacked the ship. Luckily, your mer-people found me, before I could become fish food for the wolf sharks."

The Old Man of the Sea shakes his head slowly. He gestures towards the Ruby of Seeing. "Even without using the power of this special jewel, I know that you are not telling me the whole truth, human. I will ask you one more time, why are you here in my world?"

If you decide to tell the truth, go to 2.

If you wish to try to grab the rubies, go to 28.

49

You put a hand on the innkeeper's shoulder. "Come, my friend..." you begin. But before you can continue, you feel a terrible blow on the side of your head. While your attention was on the innkeeper, one of his friends struck you with a wooden club. You drop to the floor in a heap.

"Grab him!" you hear the innkeeper shout. "He's searching for the Old Man of the Sea. The Red Queen will reward us for dealing with him!"

You try to stagger to your feet, but you are grabbed by many hands. Another blow to your head forces you into the darkness.

Go to 12.

The air around you turns bright yellow, and a ghostly figure appears before you.

You smile. "Olderon!"

"You have done well," he says, "but now the hardest task of your quest awaits you. I have discovered that you must journey to the heart of Necropolis, the City of the Dead. There you will have to fight against the creatures of your nightmares, and defeat both the Red Queen and her husband, Mortha. If you do not, then the world will fall under their control, and all will be lost."

"How do I find this city?" you ask.

"Use the rubies and trust yourself to their power." The light begins to fade.

"Will we meet again?" you ask, but there is no answer. Olderon has disappeared.

You climb onto Hergal's back, reach into the leather pouch and pull out the Ruby of Magic. "Take us to the City of the Dead..."

There is a brilliant flash of light, and the final journey of your quest begins...

1

The Ruby of Magic has revealed to you the location of Necropolis, the City of the Dead. It lies in the depths of the earth under the Mountain of the Lost.

After days of travelling on Hergal, you fly into the Valley of the Demons.

Ahead you can see the Mountain of the Lost, spewing out fire into the black night sky. The strong smell of sulphur chokes the air. This is a place of nightmares!

Suddenly dozens of firebirds appear from out of the stinking clouds. They are being ridden by skeletons armed with flaming spears. You have met these creatures before, and know how deadly they are!

If you wish to fight the creatures, go to 9.

If you wish to find another way to the mountain, go to 44.

Continue the adventure in the final book in the Blood Crown quest:

BLOOD CROWN QUEST 4
CITY OF THE DEAD

About the 2Steves

"The 2Steves" are
Britain's most popular
writing double act
for young people,
specialising in comedy
and adventure. They

perform regularly in schools and libraries,
and at festivals, taking the power of words
and story to audiences of all ages.

Together they have written many books,
including the *Crime Team* and *iHorror* series.

About the illustrator: Jack Lawrence

Jack Lawrence is a successful freelance
comics illustrator, working on titles such as
A.T.O.M., Cartoon Network, *Doctor Who
Adventures*, *2000 AD*, *Gogos Mega Metropolis*
and *Spider-Man Tower of Power*. He also works
as a freelance toy designer.

Jack lives in Maidstone in Kent with
his partner and two cats.

Want to read more "You Are The Hero" adventures? Well, why not try these...

A millionaire is found at his luxury island home – dead! But no one can work out how he died. You must get to Skull Island and solve the mystery before his killer escapes.

The daughter of a Hong Kong businessman has been kidnapped. You must find her, but who took her and why? You must crack the case, before it's too late!

You must solve the clues to stop a terrorist attack in London. But who is planning the attack, and when will it take place? It's a race against time!

An armoured convoy has been attacked in Moscow and hundreds of gold bars stolen. But who was behind the raid, and where is the gold? Get the clues — get the gold.

Also by the 2Steves: iHorror
Fight your fear. Choose your fate.

978 1 40830 985 8 pb
978 1 40831 476 0 eBook

978 1 40830 986 5 pb
978 1 40831 477 7 eBook

978 1 40830 988 9 pb
978 1 40831 479 1 eBook

978 1 40830 987 2 pb
978 1 40831 478 4 eBook

www.orchardbooks.co.uk